Scholastic Success With

BRAIN PLAY™

1st-3rd Grade

Workbook

NEW YORK • TORONTO • LONDON • AUCKLAND • SYDNEY
MEXICO CITY • NEW DELHI • HONG KONG • BUENOS AIRES

Acknowledgments

From *SCHOLASTIC SUCCESS WITH MATH WORKBOOK, Grade 3*. Published by Scholastic Professional Books/Scholastic Inc. Copyright © 2002 by Scholastic Inc. Reprinted with permission.

From *SCHOLASTIC SUCCESS WITH READING WORKBOOK, Grade 3*. Published by Scholastic Professional Books/Scholastic Inc. Copyright © 2002 by Scholastic Inc. Reprinted with permission.

From *SCHOLASTIC SUCCESS WITH WRITING WORKBOOK, Grade 3*. Published by Scholastic Professional Books/Scholastic Inc. Copyright © 2002 by Scholastic Inc. Reprinted with permission.

From *SCHOLASTIC SUCCESS WITH GRAMMAR WORKBOOK, Grade 3*. Published by Scholastic Professional Books/Scholastic Inc. Copyright © 2002 by Scholastic Inc. Reprinted with permission.

Cover art by Anne Kennedy
Cover design by Anna Christian
Interior illustrations by Jon Buller, Micheal Denman, Reggie Holladay, Susan Hendron, Anne Kennedy, Kathy Marlin, Bob Masheris, and Mark Mason
Interior design by Quack & Company

ISBN 0-439-82361-7

1 2 3 4 5 6 7 8 9 10 23 09 08 07 06 05

READING COMPREHENSION

The Milky Way

*The **main idea** of a story tells what the story is mostly about. **Details** in a story tell more information about the main idea.*

What do you think of when you hear the words, "Milky Way"? Do you think of a candy bar? Well, there is another Milky Way, and you live in it! It is our galaxy. A galaxy is a grouping of stars. Scientists have learned that there are many galaxies in outer space. The Milky Way is a spiral-shaped galaxy with swirls of stars spinning out from the center of it. Scientists believe there are about 200 billion stars in the Milky Way. One of those stars is the sun. Nine planets orbit the sun. One of them is Earth. Even from Earth, on a clear night away from city lights, you can see part of the Milky Way. It is called that because so many stars close together look like a milky white stripe across the sky. However, if you looked at it with a telescope, you would see that it is made up of thousands of stars.

Complete the main idea and each detail about the story.

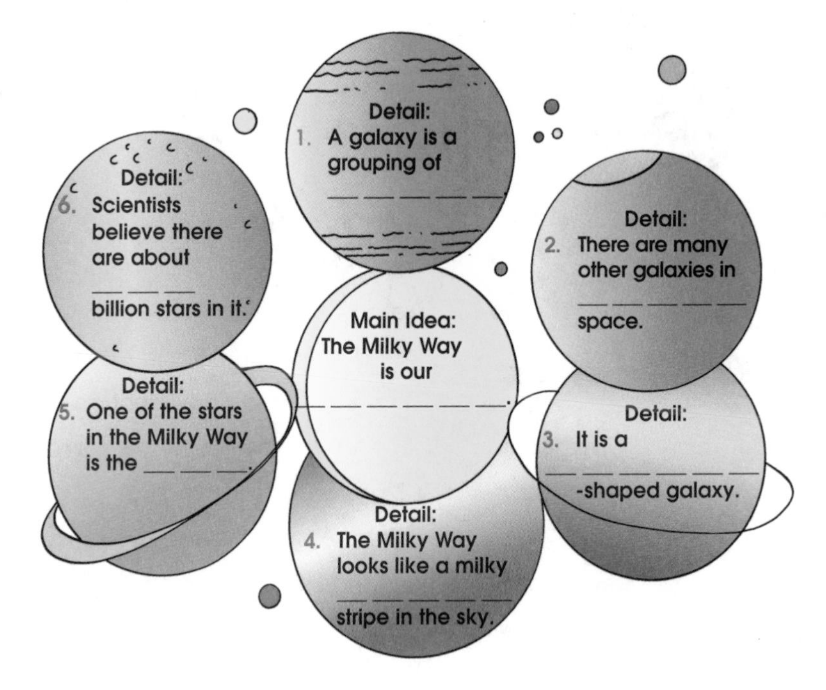

Best Friends

Amy dreaded recess every day. She did not have any friends to play with. All the girls in her class were paired up with a best friend or in groups, and she always felt left out. So, instead of playing with anyone, Amy just walked around by herself. She wanted to seesaw, but that is something you need to do with a friend. She liked to swing, but she could not go very high. She wished someone would push her to get her started.

One day, the teacher, Mrs. Gibbs, walked up and put her arm around Amy. "What's the matter, Amy? Why don't you play with the other children?" she asked kindly.

Amy replied, "Everyone has a friend except me. I don't have anyone." Mrs. Gibbs smiled and said, "Amy, the way to get a friend is to be a friend." Amy asked, "How do I do that?"

Mrs. Gibbs answered, "Look around the playground. There are three classes of third-graders out here during this recess time. Find someone who is alone and needs a friend. Then go to that person and ask them to play." Amy said she would think about it, but she was afraid she would be too embarrassed. She wasn't sure she could do it.

The next day, Amy noticed a dark-haired girl all alone on the playground. She worked up her courage and walked over to the girl. "Hi! My name is Amy. Do you want to play with me?" she asked.

"Okay," the girl said shyly. As they took turns pushing each other on the swings, Amy found out that the girl's name was Ming. She and her family had just moved from Japan. She did not know anyone and could not speak much English yet. She needed a friend.

"Want to seesaw?" Amy asked. Ming looked puzzled. Amy pointed to the seesaw. Ming smiled and nodded. Amy was so happy. She finally had a friend!

On each blank, write the letter of the picture that correctly answers the question. One answer is used twice.

1. Where does this story take place? ________

2. Who is the main character in the story? ________

   Who are the other two characters in the story? ________ and ________

3. What is the problem in the story? ________

4. How does Amy solve her problem? ________

5. What is Ming's problem? ________

   How does Ming's problem get solved? ________

A.
Mrs. Gibbs
B.
playground
C.
Ming needed a friend, too.
D.
Ming
E.
Amy
F.
Amy asked Ming to play, and they became friends.
G.
Amy needed a friend.

Scrambled Eggs

Sequencing *means putting the events of a story in the order in which they happened.*

The sentences below are scrambled. Number them in the correct sequence.

A. ____ I took a shower.
____ I got out of bed.
____ I got dressed.

B. ____ She planted the seeds.
____ Big pink flowers bloomed.
____ Tiny green shoots came up.

C. ____ He ate the sandwich.
____ He spread some jelly on them.
____ He got out two pieces of bread.

D. ____ He slid down the slide.
____ He climbed up the ladder.
____ He landed on his feet.

E. ____ We built a snowman.
____ Low gray clouds drifted in.
____ It began to snow hard.

F. ____ Firefighters put out the fire.
____ Lightning struck the barn.
____ The barn caught on fire.

G. ____ The pepper spilled out of the jar.
____ I sneezed.
____ My nose began to itch.

H. ____ "My name is Emma."
____ "Hi, what is your name?"
____ "It's nice to meet you, Emma."

I. ____ I said, "Okay, do a trick first."
____ Rover whined for a treat.
____ I gave him a dog biscuit.
____ He danced on his hind legs.

J. ____ She built a nest.
____ Baby birds hatched from the eggs.
____ I saw a robin gathering straw.
____ She laid four blue eggs.

Berry Colorful Ink

When sequencing a story, look for key words such as first, then, next, and finally to help you determine the correct sequence.

In early American schools, students used a quill pen and ink to practice writing letters and numerals. Since these schools did not have many supplies, the students often had to make their own ink at home. There were many different ways to make ink. One of the most common ways was to use berries such as blackberries, blueberries, cherries, elderberries, or strawberries. The type of berry used depended on the color of ink a student wanted. First, the type of berry to be used had to be gathered. Then a strainer was filled with the berries and held over a bowl. Next, using the back of a wooden spoon, the berries were crushed. This caused the juice to strain into the bowl. After all the berry juice was strained into the bowl, salt and vinegar were added to the juice and then stirred. Finally, the juice was stored in a small jar with a tight-fitting lid. Not only did the students make colorful inks to use, they also made invisible and glow-in-the dark inks.

Number the phrases below in the order given in the story.

_____ The mixture was stirred.

_____ Using the back of a wooden spoon, the berries were crushed.

_____ The ink was stored in a small jar with a tight-fitting lid.

_____ Berries were gathered.

_____ All the berry juice was strained into the bowl.

_____ The strainer was held over a bowl.

_____ Salt and vinegar were added to the berry juice.

_____ A strainer was filled with berries.

Where Am I?

Making inferences *means to use information in a story to make judgments about information not given in the story.*

Read each riddle below. Look for clues to help you answer each question.

1. It is dark in here. I hear bats flying. With my flashlight, I see stalactites hanging above me. I hear water dripping. Where am I?

   ____

2. Let's sit in the front row! Ha ha ha! That's funny . . . a cartoon about a drink cup that is singing to a candy bar. That makes me hungry. I think I'll go get some popcorn before it starts. Where am I?

   ____

3. This thing keeps going faster and faster, up and down, and over and around. It tickles my tummy. The girls behind me are screaming. I hope I don't go flying out of my seat! Where am I?

   ____

4. I can see rivers and highways that look like tiny ribbons. I am glad I got to sit by the window. Wow, we are in a cloud! Yes, ma'am. I would like a drink. Thank you. Where am I?

   ____

5. I am all dressed up, sitting here quietly with my parents. The flowers are pretty. The music is starting. Here she comes down the aisle. I wish they would hurry so I can have some cake! Where am I?

____

6. Doctor, can you help my dog? His name is Champ. He was bitten by a snake, and his leg is swollen. I hope he will be all right. Where am I?

____

7. How will I ever decide? Look at all the different kinds. There are red hots, chocolates, candy corn, gummy worms, jawbreakers, and lollipops. Boy, this is my favorite place in the mall! Where am I?

____

8. This row has carrots growing, and this one has onions. The corn is getting tall. The soil feels dry. I better water the plants today. Don't you think so, Mr. Scarecrow? Where am I?

____

Special Charts

***Comparing** and **contrasting** means to show the similarities and differences of things. A Venn diagram is a chart made of overlapping circles that can be used to organize the similarities and differences. The overlapping parts of the circles show how things are similar. The other part of the circles show how things are different.*

Joe, Kim, and Rob each got a lunch tray, went through the lunch line, and sat together to eat. These students all had the same lunch menu, but each one only ate what he or she liked. Joe ate chicken nuggets, green beans, applesauce, and carrots. Rob ate chicken nuggets, green beans, a roll, and corn. Kim ate chicken nuggets, a roll, applesauce, and salad.

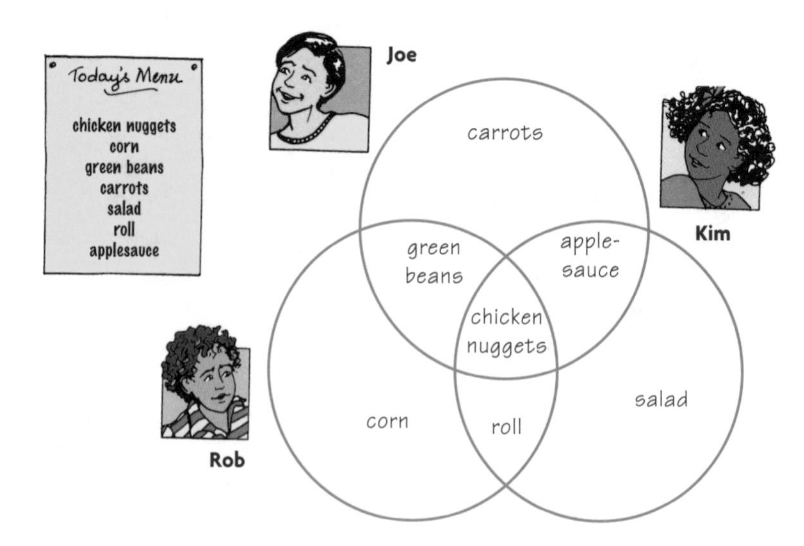

1. What food did all three students eat?

____

2. What did Joe and Rob eat that Kim did not?

____

3. What did Joe and Kim eat that Rob did not?

____

4. What did Kim and Rob eat that Joe did not?

____

5. What did Joe eat that no one else ate?

____

6. What did Rob eat that no one else ate?

____

7. What did Kim eat that no one else ate?

____

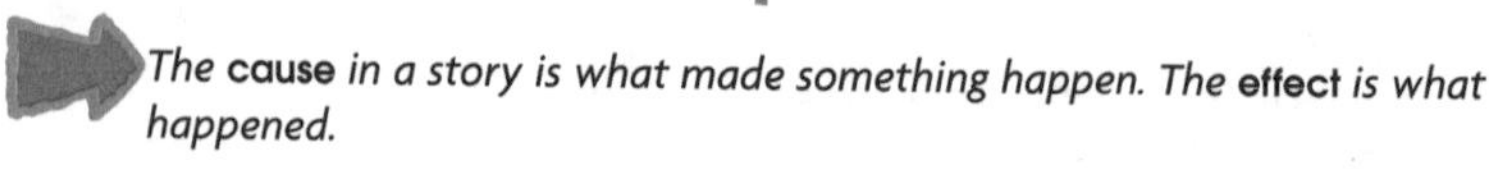

Earthquake!

The **cause** *in a story is what made something happen. The* **effect** *is what happened.*

Earthquakes are one of the most powerful events on the earth. When large sections of underground rock break and move suddenly, an earthquake occurs. This causes the ground to shake back and forth. Small earthquakes do not cause much damage, but large ones do. Some earthquakes have caused buildings and bridges to fall. Others have caused rivers to change their paths. Earthquakes near mountains and cliffs can cause landslides that cover up the houses and roads below. If a large earthquake occurs under the ocean, it can cause giant waves which flood the seashore. When large earthquakes occur in a city, there is danger of fire from broken gas lines and electric lines. Broken telephone lines and damaged roads make it difficult for rescue workers to help people who are in need. Scientists are trying to find ways to predict when an earthquake will happen so that people can be warned ahead of time.

Draw a shaky line under each effect.

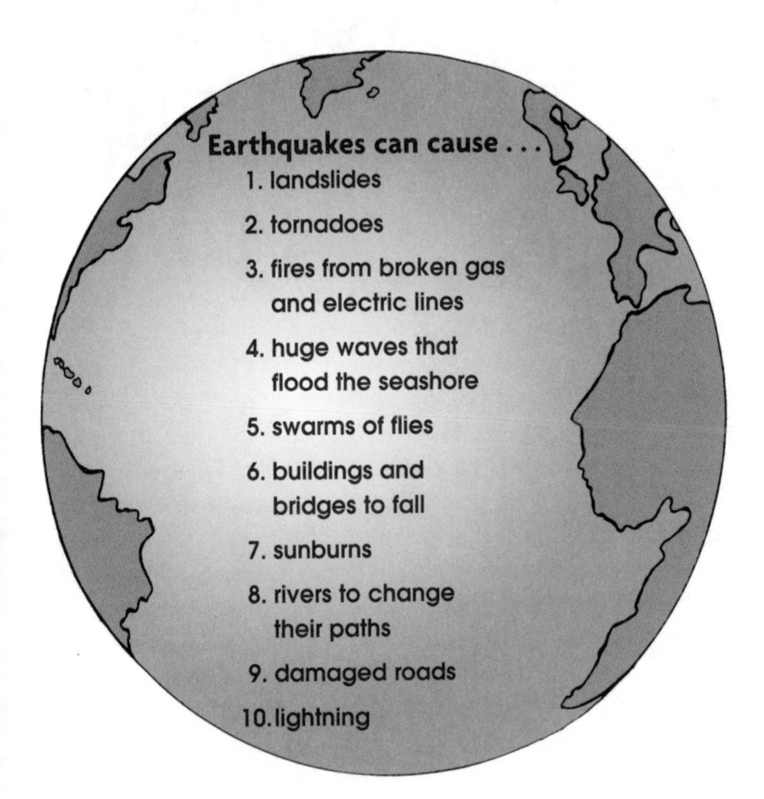

Monroe's Mighty Youth Tonic

Way back yonder in 1853, a traveling salesman named "Shifty" Sam Monroe rode into our little town of Dry Gulch. I was there that day when Shifty stood on the steps of his **buckboard** selling Monroe's Mighty Youth Tonic. Shifty announced, "Ladies and gentlemen, **lend me your ears**. I, Sam Monroe, have invented a tonic that will give you back your youth. It will **put a spring in your step**. You'll feel years younger if you take a spoonful of this **heavenly elixir** once a day. It contains a **special blend of secret ingredients**. Why, it once made a 94-year-old cowboy feel so young, he went back to **bustin' broncs** again! An old settler that was over 100 felt so young he let out a **war whoop** that could be heard in Pike County! **It's a steal** at only one dollar a bottle. Step right up and get yours now." Well, I wondered what those secret ingredients were, so I bought a bottle and tasted it. It tasted like nothing but sugar water. So I hid behind Shifty Sam's wagon and waited for the crowd to **mosey** on home. When Shifty went inside to make some more tonic, I **kept my eye on him**. Sure enough, he mixed sugar and water and added a drop of vanilla. We'd been **hornswoggled**! I **hightailed it** right then over to the sheriff's office and had him arrest that no-good varmint. Old Shifty is now spending the rest of his "mighty youth" **behind bars**!

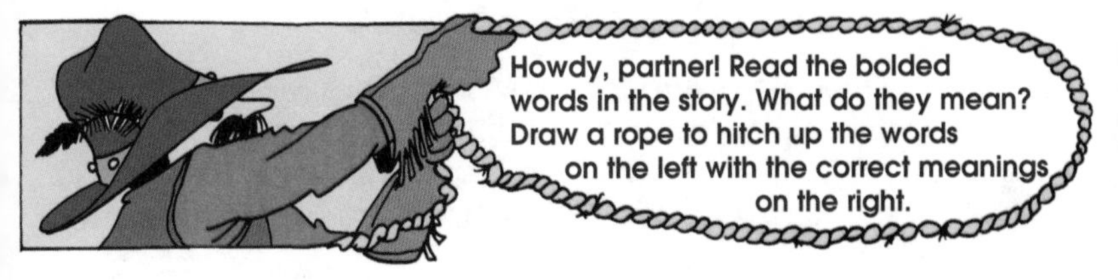

1. way back yonder	walk slowly
2. buckboard	cheated; tricked
3. Lend me your ears.	watched him closely
4. Put a spring in your step.	making wild horses gentle
5. heavenly elixir	ran quickly
6. special blend of secret ingredients	evil creature
	Listen to me.
7. bustin' broncs	in jail
8. war whoop	wagon
9. It's a steal!	You are getting it for a low price.
10. mosey	
11. kept my eye on him	I won't tell what's in it.
12. hornswoggled	makes you feel peppy
13. hightailed it	many years ago
14. no-good varmint	loud yell
15. behind bars	wonderful tonic

The Pyramid Game

Every morning before school, Mrs. Cavazos writes five words inside a pyramid on the chalkboard. When class begins, her students are to think of a title for the group of words. The title is to tell how the words are alike. The class then thinks of three words to add to the list.

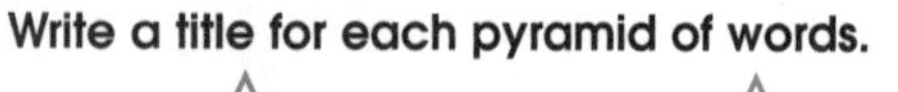

Write a title for each pyramid of words.

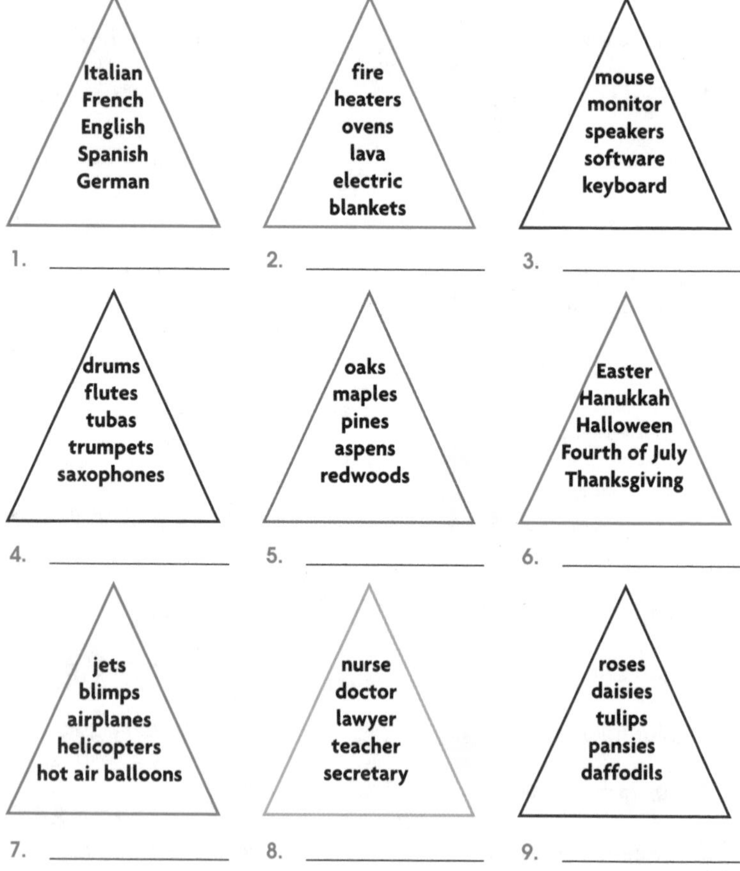

GRAMMAR

Statements and Questions

A **statement** *is a sentence that tells something. It ends with a period. A* **question** *is a sentence that asks something. It ends with a question mark.*

A. Read each sentence. Write Q on the line if the sentence is a question. Write S if the sentence is a statement.

1. Where did the ant live? ______
2. The ant had many cousins. ______
3. She found the crumb under a leaf. ______
4. How will she carry it? ______
5. Who came along first? ______
6. The lizard wouldn't help. ______
7. He said he was too cold. ______
8. Why did the rooster fly away? ______

Statements and Questions

*A **statement** is a sentence that tells something. It ends with a period. A **question** is a sentence that asks something. It ends with a question mark.*

A. Rewrite each sentence correctly. Begin each sentence with a capital letter. Use periods and question marks correctly.

1. can we take a taxi downtown

____

2. where does the bus go

____

3. the people on the bus waved to us

____

4. we got on the elevator

____

5. should I push the elevator button

____

Exclamations and Commands

*An **exclamation** is a sentence that shows strong feeling. It ends with an exclamation point. A **command** is a sentence that gives an order. It ends with a period.*

A. Read each sentence. Write *E* on the line if the sentence is an exclamation. Write *C* if the sentence is a command.

1. They chase buffaloes! _____
2. You have to go, too. _____
3. Wait at the airport. _____
4. It snows all the time! _____
5. Alligators live in the sewers! _____
6. Look at the horse. _____
7. That's a great-looking horse! _____
8. Write a letter to Seymour. _____

Exclamations and Commands

Look at the underlined part of each sentence. Decide if it is correct. Fill in the bubble next to the correct answer.

1. I'm going to Texas!
   - ◯ I'm going to Texas?
   - ◯ I'm to Texas!
   - ◯ correct as is

2. I am so excited
   - ◯ excited!
   - ◯ excited?
   - ◯ correct as is

3. Please help me pack!
   - ◯ pack?
   - ◯ pack.
   - ◯ correct as is

4. Her baby brother is adorable
   - ◯ adorable?
   - ◯ adorable!
   - ◯ correct as is

5. I can't wait!
   - ◯ wait.
   - ◯ wait
   - ◯ correct as is

6. Help me find.
   - ◯ Help me find a game.
   - ◯ Help find game.
   - ◯ correct as is

7. We'll have such fun!
   - ◯ fun
   - ◯ fun?
   - ◯ correct as is

8. It be!
   - ◯ It will be great!
   - ◯ It great!
   - ◯ correct as is

9. Remember to write to me
   - ◯ to write to
   - ◯ to write to me.
   - ◯ correct as is

10. My team the game!
    - ◯ team won the game!
    - ◯ team won game!
    - ◯ correct as is

Singular and Plural Nouns

A ***singular noun*** *names one person, place, or thing. A* ***plural noun*** *names more than one person, place, or thing. Add -s to form the plural of most nouns.*

A. Each sentence has an underlined noun. On the line, write *S* if it is a singular noun. Write *P* if it is a plural noun.

1. She has a new baby. ______
2. It is very cute. ______
3. She has small fingers. ______
4. She drinks from a bottle. ______
5. I can tell my friends all about it. ______

B. Read each sentence. Underline the singular noun. Circle the plural noun.

1. The baby has two sisters.
2. The nightgown has pockets.
3. Her hand has tiny fingers.
4. My parents have a baby.
5. The family has three girls.

Singular and Plural Nouns

A **singular noun** *names one person, place, or thing. A* **plural noun** *names more than one person, place, or thing. Add* **-s** *to form the plural of most nouns. Add* **-es** *to form the plural of nouns that end in* **ss**, **x**, **ch**, *or* **sh**. *Some nouns change their spelling to form the plural.*

A. Finish the chart. Write singular nouns in each column.

Nouns that end in *ch, sh, ss, x*	Nouns that end in *y*	Nouns that end in *f*
bench	party	loaf

B. Complete each sentence with the plural form of the noun in ( ).

1. Mia picks ______________ from the trees in her backyard. (cherry)

2. There are also many ______________ with tiny berries. (bush)

3. Fresh ______________ are her favorite snack. (peach)

4. She loads ______________ with these different fruits. (box)

5. The kitchen ______________ are filled with delicious jams. (shelf)

6. Mia shares the fruit with the third-grade ______________. (class)

Singular and Plural Nouns

Read each riddle. Decide if the underlined noun is correct. Fill in the bubble next to the correct answer.

1. We are square and made from cardboard. We are boxs.
   - ○ boxes
   - ○ box
   - ○ correct as is

2. We help you chew your food. We are tooth.
   - ○ tooths
   - ○ teeth
   - ○ correct as is

3. You can find us on a farm. We are geese.
   - ○ goose
   - ○ gooses
   - ○ correct as is

4. Be sure not to drop us when you take a drink. We are glassess.
   - ○ glass
   - ○ glasses
   - ○ correct as is

5. We are messages sent over telephone lines. We are fax.
   - ○ faxs
   - ○ faxes
   - ○ correct as is

6. You can use us to comb your hair. We are brush.

- ⬭ brushes
- ⬭ brushs
- ⬭ correct as is

7. You can buy us in a food store. We are grocerys.

- ⬭ grocery
- ⬭ groceries
- ⬭ correct as is

8. We are places trains can stop. We are stations.

- ⬭ station
- ⬭ stationes
- ⬭ correct as is

9. We like to eat cheese. We are mouse.

- ⬭ mice
- ⬭ mices
- ⬭ correct as is

10. We are tales to read. We are story.

- ⬭ stories
- ⬭ storys
- ⬭ correct as is

Common and Proper Nouns

A **common noun** *names any person, place, or thing. A* **proper noun** *names a particular person, place, or thing. A proper noun begins with a capital letter.*

A. Is the underlined word a common noun or a proper noun? Write *common* or *proper*.

1. The girl likes to learn. ____________
2. She goes to two schools. ____________
3. She lives in America. ____________

B. Underline the common nouns. Circle the proper nouns.

1. April has a brother and a sister.
2. Their names are Julius and May.
3. Their parents were born in Taiwan.
4. April goes to school on Saturday.
5. She is learning a language called Mandarin.
6. May read a book about the Middle Ages.

Action Verbs

Action verbs *are words that tell what the subject of the sentence does.*

A. Underline the action verb in each sentence.

1. The villagers cheered loudly.
2. They added flavor to the cheese.
3. Please give them the milk.
4. He serves the cheese.
5. He emptied the buckets.

B. Circle the action verb in ( ) that paints a more vivid picture of what the subject is doing.

1. The villagers (walked, paraded) across the floor.
2. Father (whispered, talked) to the baby.
3. The puppy (ate, gobbled) down his food.
4. The girl (skipped, went) to her chair.
5. The ball (fell, bounced) down the stairs.

Action Verbs

A. Fill in the bubble next to the action verb in each sentence.

1. Crystal's whole family arrived for dinner.
   - ⬭ dinner
   - ⬭ family
   - ⬭ arrived

2. Her grandmother hugged everyone.
   - ⬭ grandmother
   - ⬭ hugged
   - ⬭ everyone

3. Her aunt and uncle roasted a huge turkey.
   - ⬭ roasted
   - ⬭ turkey
   - ⬭ huge

4. Everyone ate the delicious meal.
   - ⬭ ate
   - ⬭ Everyone
   - ⬭ meal

5. They cheered for the cooks!
   - ⬭ cooks
   - ⬭ They
   - ⬭ cheered

B. Read each sentence. Fill in the bubble next to the more vivid verb.

1. The puppy ____ after the ball.
   ⬭ went
   ⬭ chased

2. She ____ all around the house and yard.
   ⬭ dashed
   ⬭ went

3. A yellow cat ____ through the wooden fence.
   ⬭ looked
   ⬭ peeked

4. Then the puppy ____ high into the air.
   ⬭ leaped
   ⬭ moved

5. She ____ the ball.
   ⬭ got
   ⬭ grabbed

Subjects and Predicates

The **complete subject** *tells whom or what the sentence is about. The* **complete predicate** *tells who or what the subject is or does. The* **simple subject** *is the main word in the complete subject. The* **simple predicate** *is the verb in the complete predicate.*

A. Is the underlined part of the sentence the complete subject or a complete predicate? Fill in the bubble next to the correct answer.

1. <u>My little brother</u> carried his backpack.
   - ◯ complete subject
   - ◯ complete predicate

2. I <u>found my old fishing rod</u>.
   - ◯ complete subject
   - ◯ complete predicate

3. <u>My dad</u> put air in our bicycle tires.
   - ◯ complete subject
   - ◯ complete predicate

4. Our whole family <u>rode to the big lake</u>.
   - ◯ complete subject
   - ◯ complete predicate

5. <u>Many pink flowers</u> bloomed on the trees.
   - ◯ complete subject
   - ◯ complete predicate

B. Fill in the bubble that tells if the underlined word is the simple subject or the simple predicate.

1. A man <u>rowed</u> a boat on the lake.
   ⬭ simple subject
   ⬭ simple predicate

2. My <u>brother</u> played ball in the field.
   ⬭ simple subject
   ⬭ simple predicate

3. Some other <u>children</u> joined in the game.
   ⬭ simple subject
   ⬭ simple predicate

4. Our large <u>basket</u> sat unopened on the picnic table.
   ⬭ simple subject
   ⬭ simple predicate

5. We <u>ate</u> cheese sandwiches and fruit.
   ⬭ simple subject
   ⬭ simple predicate

Adjectives

*An **adjective** is a word that describes a person, place, or thing.*

A. Read each sentence. Fill in the bubble next to the word that is an adjective.

1. Several relatives from Mexico visited us.
   - ⬭ Several
   - ⬭ relatives
   - ⬭ visited

2. The trip took six hours.
   - ⬭ trip
   - ⬭ six
   - ⬭ hours

3. They took many pictures of my family.
   - ⬭ took
   - ⬭ many
   - ⬭ pictures

4. My uncle wore a blue hat.
   - ⬭ uncle
   - ⬭ blue
   - ⬭ hat

5. My aunt wore a colorful serape.
   - ⬭ aunt
   - ⬭ wore
   - ⬭ colorful

B. Fill in the bubble next to the adjective that best completes the sentence.

1. We ate the ____ food.
   - ⬭ loud
   - ⬭ fuzzy
   - ⬭ delicious

2. There were ____ people in the restaurant.
   - ⬭ one
   - ⬭ many
   - ⬭ green

3. My dad ordered ____ tortillas.
   - ⬭ sharp
   - ⬭ loud
   - ⬭ some

4. My cousin José ate ____ tamales!
   - ⬭ noisy
   - ⬭ five
   - ⬭ curly

5. Everyone had a ____ time!
   - ⬭ cold
   - ⬭ wonderful
   - ⬭ purple

Possessive Nouns

A **possessive noun** *shows ownership. Add* **'s** *to make a singular noun show ownership. Add an apostrophe (') after the* **s** *of a plural noun to show ownership.*

A. Underline the possessive noun in each sentence. Write *S* on the line if the possessive noun is singular. Write *P* if the possessive noun is plural.

1. Anna's family took a walk in the woods. ______
2. They saw two birds' nests high up in a tree. ______
3. A yellow butterfly landed on Brad's backpack. ______
4. Anna liked the pattern of the butterfly's wings. ______
5. A turtle's shell had many spots. ______
6. Anna took pictures of two chipmunks' homes. ______
7. The animals' tails had dark stripes. ______

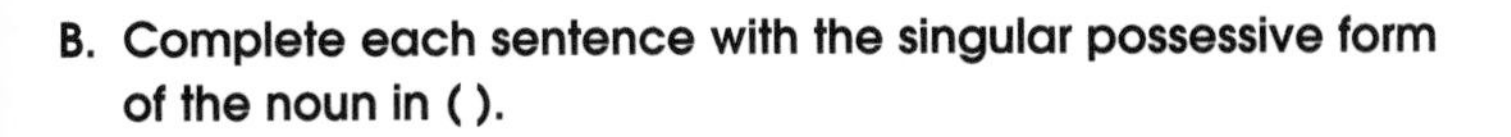

B. Complete each sentence with the singular possessive form of the noun in ( ).

1. Jim was going to play basketball at ________________ house. (Carol)

2. One of ________________ new sneakers was missing. (Jim)

3. He looked under his ________________ desk. (sister)

4. He crawled under his ________________ bed to look. (brother)

5. It was outside in his ________________ flower garden. (dad)

6. The ________________ lace had been chewed. (sneaker)

7. Jim saw his ________________ footprints in the dirt. (dog)

Using Punctuation

Quotation marks *show the exact words of a speaker.* **Commas** *appear between the day and year in a date, between the city and state in a location, and between the lines of an address.*

A. Add quotation marks to show the speaker's exact words.

1. I have a strange case, said Mr. Brown.
2. What's strange about it? asked Encyclopedia.
3. Seventeen years ago Mr. Hunt found an elephant, began Mr. Brown.
4. Where did he find it? asked Mrs. Brown.
5. The elephant just appeared in his window, answered Mr. Brown.
6. He must have fainted! exclaimed Encyclopedia.
7. No, Mr. Hunt bought him, said Mr. Brown.

B. Add commas wherever they are needed.

1. I go to the library in Huntsville Alabama.
2. It is located at 12 Oak Street Huntsville Alabama 36554.
3. The last time I was there was January 8 2001.
4. The books I checked out were due January 22 2001.
5. My cousin Jeb goes to the branch library at 75 Peachtree Lane Farley Alabama 35802.
6. Is it true that Donald Sobol once spoke at the library in Redstone Park Alabama?
7. He spoke there on September 29 2000.
8. He will soon read at 47 Draper Road Newportville Pennsylvania.

Using Punctuation

Quotation marks *show the exact words of a speaker.* **Commas** *appear between the day and year in a date, between the city and state in a location, between the lines of an address, and after all but the last item in a series. Underlining shows book titles.*

A. Read each sentence. Add any missing commas.

1. Mrs. Wu's bank is located at 92 Maple Avenue Inwood Texas 75209.
2. She opened an account there on September 8 2001.
3. She also uses the branch office in Lakewood Texas.
4. That branch is open weekdays Saturdays and some evenings.
5. The main office is closed Saturdays Sundays and all holidays.
6. Mrs. Wu saw Ms. Ames Mr. Pacheco and Mrs. Jefferson at the bank on Saturday.
7. They carried checks bills and deposits.
8. Mr. Pacheco has had an account at that bank since May 2 1974.

B. Read the sentences below. Add any missing quotation marks, commas, or underlining.

1. My favorite author is Jerry Spinelli said Rick.

2. Spinelli was born on February 1 1941.

3. His home town is Norristown Pennsylvania.

4. What are your favorite books by him? asked Teresa.

5. I like Maniac Magee Dump Days and Fourth Grade Rats   replied Rick.

Contractions

A **contraction** *is a shortened form of two words. An* **apostrophe** *(') is used to show where one or more letters have been left out.*

A. Fill in the bubble next to the two words that make up the underlined contraction.

1. We're going to see a nature movie.
- ⬭ We have
- ⬭ We is
- ⬭ We are

2. "You'll learn about living things," our teacher said.
- ⬭ You are
- ⬭ You will
- ⬭ I will

3. We've been studying animal habitats in science.
- ⬭ We have
- ⬭ We are
- ⬭ You are

4. I'm writing a report on how animals communicate.
- ⬭ I have
- ⬭ I am
- ⬭ I will

5. It's about how animals use their senses.
- ⬭ It is
- ⬭ Is not
- ⬭ He is

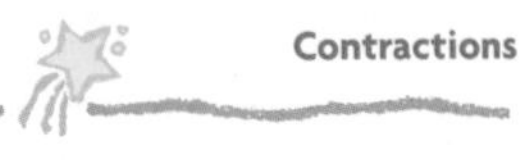

B. Fill in the bubble next to the contraction for the underlined words.

1. The teacher asked, "Who is writing about birds?"
   - ◯ Won't
   - ◯ Who's
   - ◯ What's

2. There is a new bird exhibit at the museum.
   - ◯ There's
   - ◯ They've
   - ◯ Where's

3. I hope she will be there Saturday morning.
   - ◯ she's
   - ◯ I'll
   - ◯ she'll

4. The museum does not open until 10 A.M.
   - ◯ doesn't
   - ◯ didn't
   - ◯ isn't

5. Do not forget your notebook and pencil.
   - ◯ Doesn't
   - ◯ Don't
   - ◯ Shouldn't

Contractions

A. Underline the contraction in each sentence. Circle the apostrophe. Then write the contraction on the line.

1. It's time for another adventure. ________________
2. We're studying animal habitats. ________________
3. They've made a habitat for Bella. ________________
4. I'm sure that Bella is gone. ________________
5. Wanda thinks that she'll be back. ________________
6. They're in favor of going to find Bella. ________________

B. Circle the contraction. Then write the two words that make up the contraction.

1. I've gone on this bus before. ________________
2. What's the bus doing? ________________
3. It's shrinking to the size of a bullfrog. ________________
4. The students say they're having fun. ________________
5. "I'm hanging on for dear life," Liz said. ________________

WRITING

Dinnertime

*A **sentence** is a group of words that expresses a complete thought.*
*A **fragment** is an incomplete thought.*

Write *S* for sentence or *F* for fragment.

____ **1. Insects eat many different things.**

____ **2. Some of these things.**

____ **3. The praying mantis eats other insects.**

____ **4. Water bugs eat tadpoles and small frogs.**

____ **5. Flower nectar makes good.**

____ **6. Build nests to store their food.**

____ 7. The cockroach will eat almost anything.

____ 8. Termites.

____ 9. A butterfly caterpillar.

____ 10. Bite animals and people.

____ 11. Some insects will even eat paper.

____ 12. Insects have different mouth parts to help them eat.

Wacky World

An asking sentence is called a **question***. It begins with a capital letter and ends with a question mark (?).*

Write each question correctly.

1. why is that car in a tree

____

2. should that monkey be driving a bus

____

3. did you see feathers on that crocodile

____

4. can elephants really lay eggs

____

The Dry Desert

A sentence that shows strong feeling or excitement is called an **exclamation**. *It ends with an exclamation point (!).*

Finish each sentence with a period, a question mark, or an exclamation point.

1. It is hard for plants and animals to get water in the desert
2. Can a cactus live without enough water
3. Some deserts are hot, and others are cool
4. A lizard is running toward us
5. Does a camel really store water in its hump
6. Some deserts are cold and covered with ice

7. How often does it rain in the desert

8. The largest desert is the Sahara

9. Are there any deserts in the United States

10. There is a long snake slithering across the sand

11. People who live in the desert travel to find water

12. I see water up ahead

The Sunny Sahara

Every sentence begins with a capital letter.
A statement ends with a period.
A question ends with a question mark.
An exclamation ends with an exclamation point.

Write each sentence correctly.

1. the Sahara Desert is in Africa

____

2. do people live in the Sahara Desert

____

____

3. the Sahara Desert is about the same size as the United States

4. how high is the temperature in the Sahara Desert

5. once the temperature reached 138°F

Stretch It!

A sentence includes a subject and a verb. A sentence is more interesting when it also includes a part that tells where, when, or why.

Add more information to each sentence by telling where, when, or why. Write the complete new sentence.

1. **Mom is taking us shopping.** 

____

____

2. **The stores are closing.** 

____

____

3. We need to find a gift for Dad.

4. I will buy new jeans.

Ketchup and Mustard

Sometimes two sentences can be combined to make one sentence.

Sentences that share the same subject seem to go together like ketchup and mustard. Rewrite the sentences by combining their endings with the word *and*.

1. I ordered a hamburger.

I ordered a milkshake.

I ordered a hamburger

and a milkshake.

2. I like salt on my French fries.

I like ketchup on my French fries.

3. My mom makes great pork chops.

My mom makes great applesauce.

---

4. My dad eats two huge helpings of meat loaf!

My dad eats two huge helpings of potatoes!

Buckets of Fun

A **describing word** *helps you imagine how something looks, feels, smells, sounds, or tastes.*

Write a list of describing words on each bucket to fit the bucket's category.

words that describe
how something feels
words that describe
weather
words that describe
feelings

The Great Outdoors

*A **describing word** can tell more about a subject or a verb.*

Add describing words to make each sentence more interesting.

1. The ____________ hikers walked back to camp ____________.

2. The ____________ bird sang ____________.

3. The ____________ tree grew ____________.

4. ____________ children played ____________.

5. My ____________ sister swam ____________.

6. The ____________________ crickets chirped

____________________.

7. The ____________________ flowers bloomed

____________________.

8. The ____________________ swing set creaked

____________________.

9. The ____________________ ice cream melted

____________________.

10. The ____________________ trees shook

____________________ in the storm.

What Did She Say?

Quotation marks *(" ") are used to show a character is talking in a story. They surround only the character's words.*

Fill in the speech bubbles to match the paragraph below each picture.

Daisy put on her rain boots, coat, and hat. "I think it's fun to splash in the puddles," she said.

As the rain continued, the puddles turned to streams. "Rain, rain, don't go away!" Daisy sang.

"Wow! I should have worn my bathing suit!" Daisy shouted as the water rose higher.

Then Daisy had an idea. She turned her umbrella upside down and climbed in. "It's a perfect day to go sailing," she said.

MATH

Place-Value Puzzler

What is too much fun for one, enough for two, and means nothing to three?

Find the answer to this riddle by using place value! Take a look at each number below. One digit in each number is underlined. Circle the word in each line that tells the place value of the underlined number. Write the letters next to each correct answer in the blanks below. The first one is done for you.

A.	$1\underline{5},209$	**a** thousands	**i** hundreds
B.	$4,7\underline{2}9$	**n** hundreds	**s** tens
C.	$\underline{4}25$	**e** hundreds	**o** tens
D.	$7,6\underline{1}8$	**c** tens	**g** ones
E.	$1,\underline{1}12$	**p** thousands	**r** hundreds
F.	$8,63\underline{6}$	**a** hundreds	**e** ones
G.	$2\underline{2}2$	**t** tens	**m** ones

a
____   ____ ____ ____ ____ ____ ____
A   B C D E F G

Bee Riddle

Riddle: What did the farmer get when he tried to reach the beehive?

Round each number. Then use the Decoder to solve the riddle by filling in the spaces at the bottom of the page.

1. **Round 7 to the nearest ten** ______
2. **Round 23 to the nearest ten** ______
3. **Round 46 to the nearest ten** ______
4. **Round 92 to the nearest ten** ______
5. **Round 203 to the nearest hundred** ______
6. **Round 420 to the nearest hundred** ______
7. **Round 588 to the nearest hundred** ______
8. **Round 312 to the nearest hundred** ______
9. **Round 549 to the nearest hundred** ______
10. **Round 710 to the nearest hundred** ______

Decoder

400	**A**
800	**W**
30	**O**
10	**Y**
25	**E**
500	**I**
210	**J**
20	**L**
40	**C**
700	**U**
90	**S**
100	**T**
600	**G**
95	**F**
50	**N**
550	**V**
300	**Z**
7	**H**
200	**Z**

A "B __ __ __ __" __ __ __ __ __ __

10 5 8 1 4 9 7 3 6 2

Animal Caller

A bar graph shows information. This bar graph shows the speeds of animals in miles per hour. Use the graph to answer the questions.

WHICH ANIMAL IS...

1. THE FASTEST?

____

2. THE SLOWEST?

____

3. GOING 40 mph?

____

4. 20 mph FASTER THAN A CAT?

____

5. HOW MANY 4-FOOTED ANIMALS ARE LISTED?

____

DO THE BARS SHOW...

6. ANIMAL NAMES AND mph?

____

7. SPEED OR WEIGHT?

____

8. INFORMATION ABOUT TIGERS

____

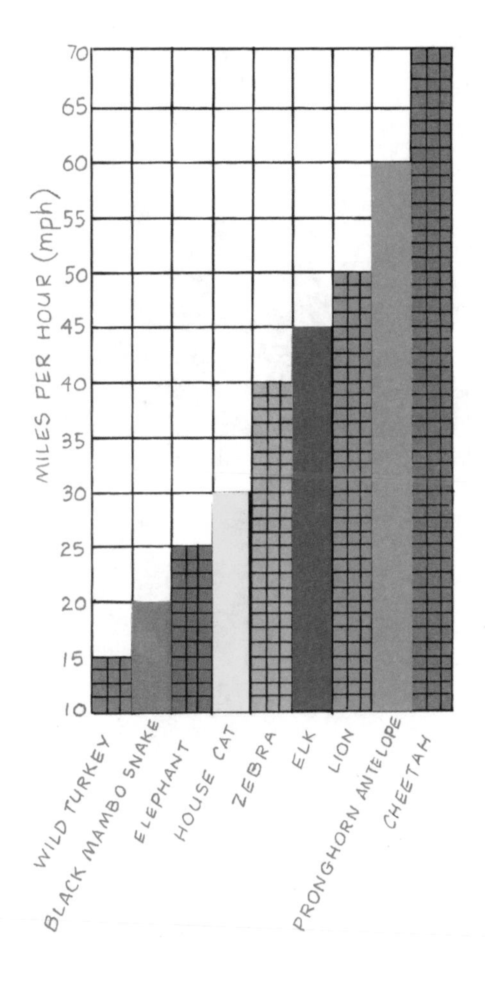
MILES PER HOUR (mph)
70
65
60
55
50
45
40
35
30
25
20
15
10
WILD TURKEY
BLACK MAMBO SNAKE
ELEPHANT
HOUSE CAT
ZEBRA
ELK
LION
PRONGHORN ANTELOPE
CHEETAH

Graph Drafter

A line graph shows how something changes over time. This line graph shows temperature changes during a year in New York City. Use the graph to answer the questions below.

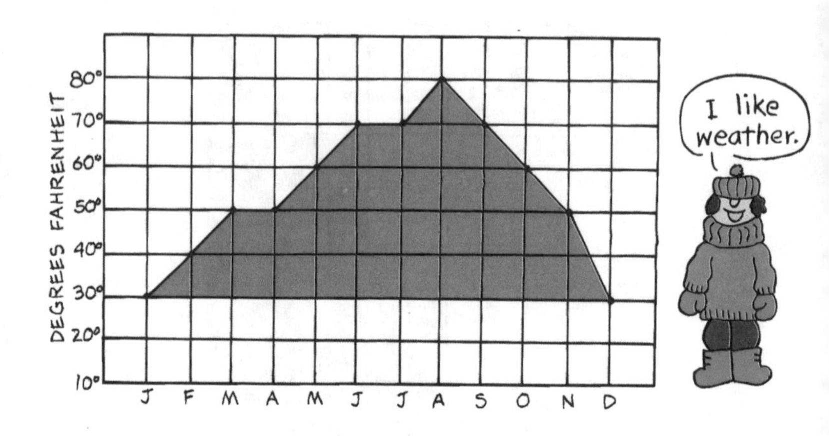

SUGGESTION: SHORTEN THE NAMES, LIKE JAN, FEB, AUG, SEP, OCT, NOV.

1. WHAT 2 MONTHS WERE THE COLDEST? ____________________

2. WHAT WAS THE TEMPERATURE OF THE HOTTEST MONTH? ________

3. WHAT MONTHS WERE 70°? ____________________

4. ANY TEMPERATURE CHANGE BETWEEN JAN. AND FEB.? ________

5. WAS THE TEMPERATURE EVER WARMER THAN AUGUST? ________

6. DID IT BECOME COLDER OR WARMER IN JUNE? ____________

7. DID THE TEMPERATURE RISE OR FALL IN OCTOBER? ________

8. WHAT MONTH IS THE 5th MONTH? ____________________

9. HOW MANY DEGREES BETWEEN 40° AND 80°? ____________

On the *Mayflower*

Add or subtract. Write the Pilgrims' names in alphabetical order by sequencing the answers from greatest to smallest.

Resolve	14 – 7 =
Susan	13 – 9 =
Jasper	6 + 7 =
Priscilla	8 + 2 =
Edward	9 + 6 =
Solomon	11 – 6 =
Prudence	18 – 9 =
Constance	8 + 8 =
Remember	17 – 9 =
Oceanus	7 + 5 =
Thomas	15 – 12 =
Samuel	14 – 8 =
Charity	6 + 12 =
Peregrine	16 – 5 =
Humility	9 + 5 =

Stars and Stripes Forever

Circle groups of 10. Write the number of tens and ones.
Write the number in the star.

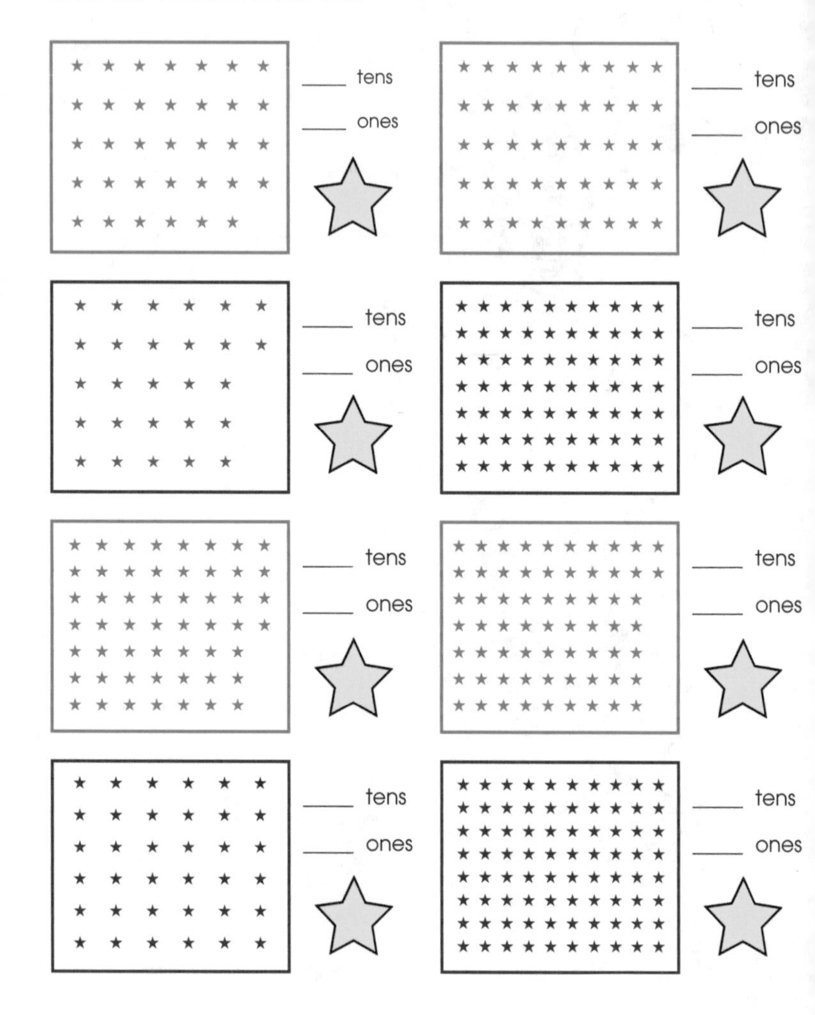

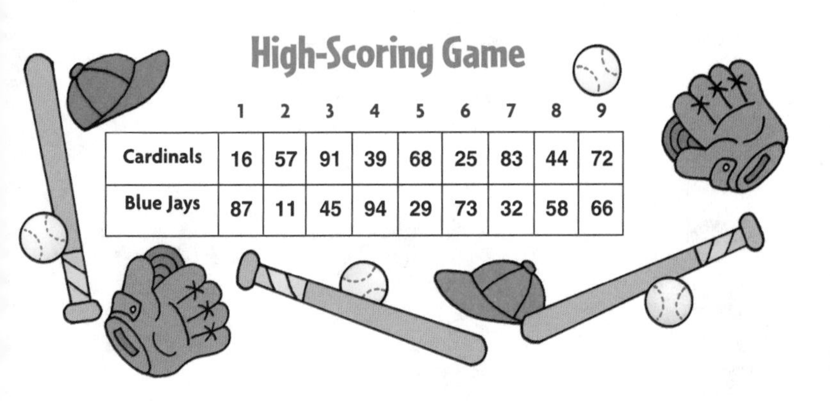

High-Scoring Game

	1	2	3	4	5	6	7	8	9
Cardinals	16	57	91	39	68	25	83	44	72
Blue Jays	87	11	45	94	29	73	32	58	66

Find the total number of runs in each inning. Add.

1	2	3	4	5	6	7	8	9
16 + 87								

Find the difference in runs in each inning. Subtract.

1	2	3	4	5	6	7	8	9
87 - 16								

It's Electrifying!

Regroup tens into hundreds. Draw a line to connect.

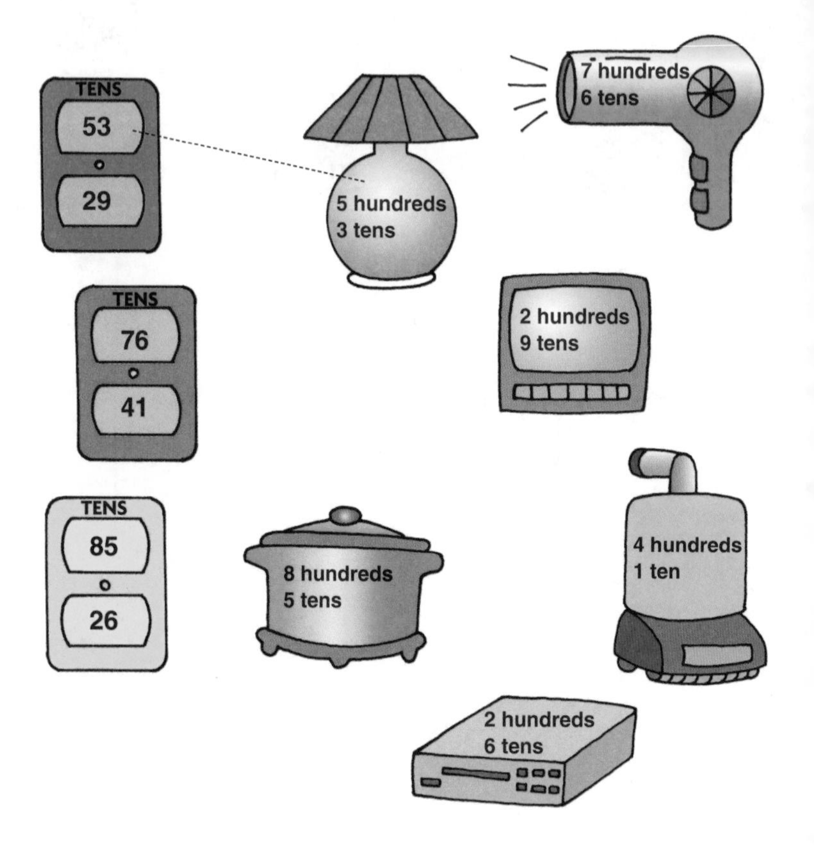

Home Sweet Home

Use the coordinates to find each number. Add or subtract.

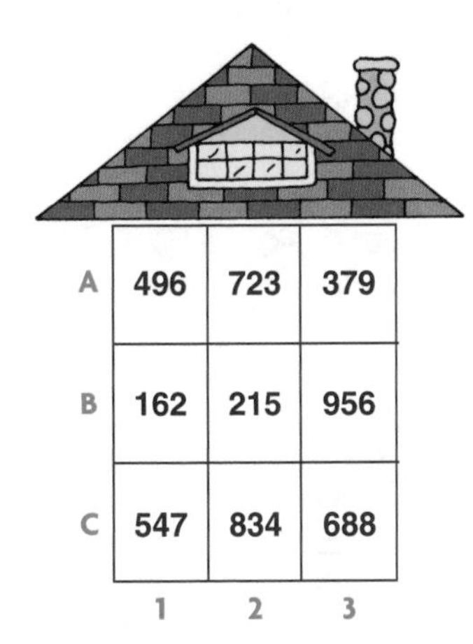

	1	2	3
A	496	723	379
B	162	215	956
C	547	834	688

	4	5	6
E	668	884	345
F	239	716	188
G	422	578	957

A. (A, 1)
(F, 6) − ______

B. (B, 3)
(E, 4) − ______

C. (C, 1)
(F, 4) + ______

D. (A, 3)
(E, 6) + ______

E. (A, 2)
(B, 1) − ______

F. (G, 4)
(B, 2) − ______

Code Zero! Code One!

When a number is multiplied by 0, the product is always 0. When a number is multiplied by 1, the product is always the number being multiplied.

Multiply. Shade all products of 0 yellow. Shade all other products green.

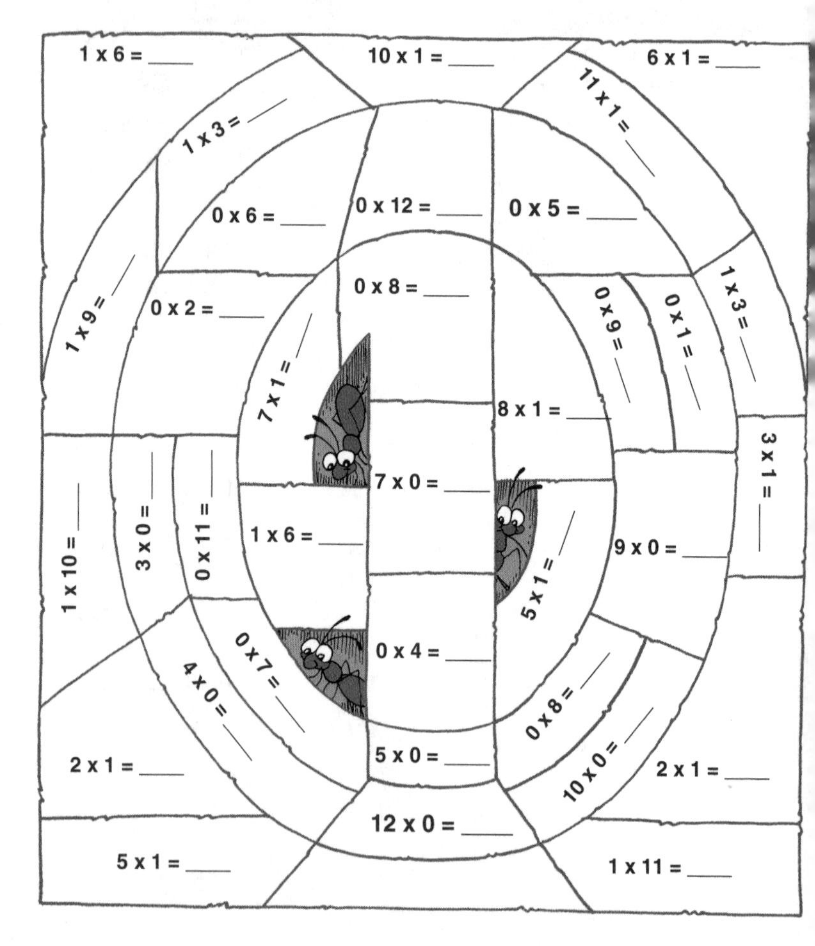

Two, Four, Six, Eight, Who Do We Appreciate?

When multiplying by 2, skip count by 2, or think of number line jumping!

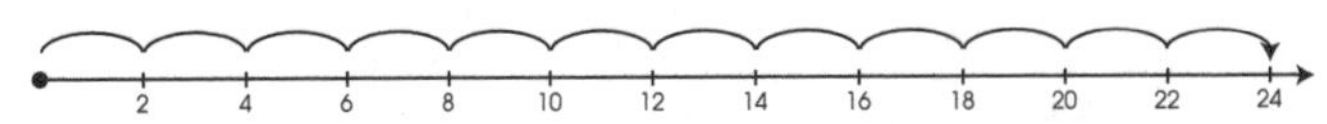

Multiply.

A.	2 x 3 = ____	2 x 8 = ____	11 x 2 = ____	2 x 7 = ____
B.	8 x 2 = ____	4 x 2 = ____	2 x 2 = ____	2 x 4 = ____
C.	12 x 2 = ____	5 x 2 = ____	10 x 2 = ____	2 x 12 = ____
D.	9 x 2 = ____	2 x 1 = ____	2 x 10 = ____	7 x 2 = ____
E.	2 x 0 = ____	2 x 6 = ____	3 x 2 = ____	0 x 2 = ____
F.	2 x 5 = ____	2 x 9 = ____		
G.	6 x 2 = ____	1 x 2 = ____		
H.	2 x 11 = ____	2 x 2 = ____		

A Positive Answer

What should you say if you are asked, "Do you want to learn the 3s?"

To find out, look at each problem below. If the product is correct, color the space green. If the product is incorrect, color the space yellow.

Puzzling Facts

Multiply. Write the number word for each product in the puzzle. Don't forget the hyphens!

Across

2. 4 x 9 = ______
4. 4 x 5 = ______
7. 4 x 3 = ______
8. 4 x 7 = ______
9. 4 x 10 = ______
11. 4 x 0 = ______
12. 4 x 11 = ______

Down

1. 4 x 4 = ______
2. 4 x 8 = ______
3. 4 x 12 = ______
5. 4 x 2 = ______
6. 4 x 6 = ______
10. 4 x 1 = ______

How Many Can You Find?

Complete each multiplication sentence. Then circle each answer in the picture.

A. 2 x 5 = ______

B. 5 x ______ = 5

C. ______ x 5 = 35

D. 10 x 5 = ______

E. ______ x 5 = 60

F. 5 x 6 = ______

G. ______ x 5 = 55

H. 5 x 3 = ______

I. 8 x 5 = ______

J. ______ x 5 = 45

K. 2 x ______ = 10

L. ______ x 5 = 25

M. 7 x 5 = ______

N. 5 x 12 = ______

O. 5 x ______ = 20

Mathematics Fireworks

Multiply. On another piece of paper, find the sum of the products of each star trail. Then use the key to color each star to match its star trail sum.

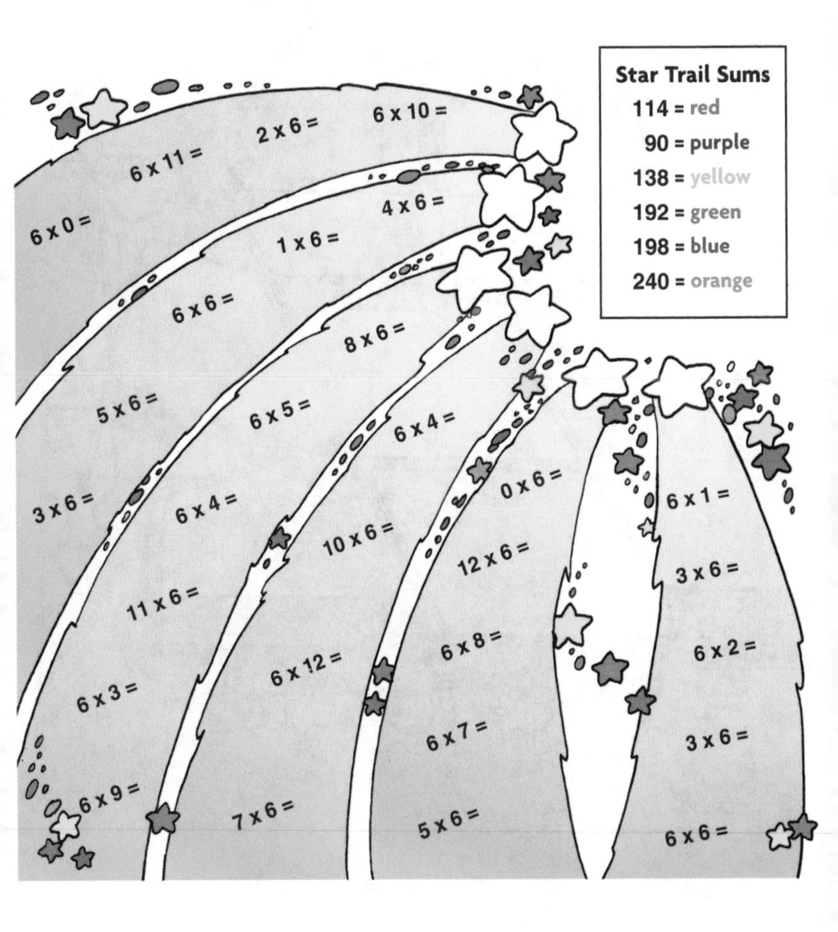

Flying Sevens

Multiply.

The Ultimate Eight Track

Use a stopwatch to time how long it takes to multiply around the track.

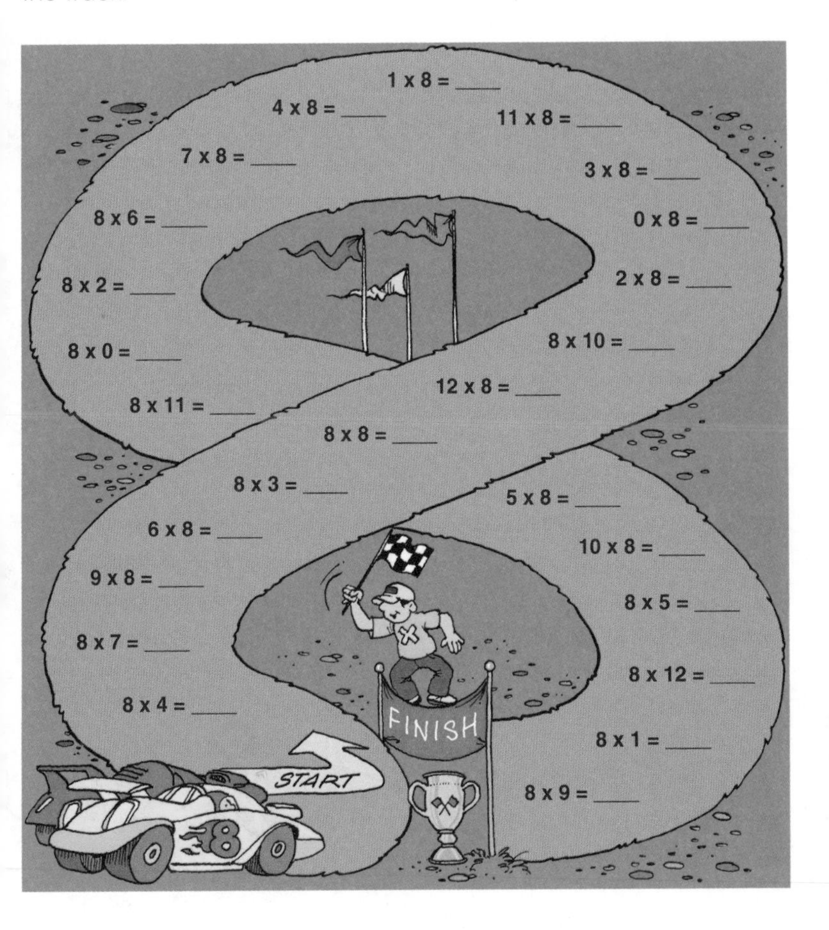

Cross-Number Puzzle

Multiply. Write the number word for each product in the puzzle. Don't forget the hyphens!

Across

1. 9 x 5 = ____
5. 1 x 9 = ____
7. 9 x 12 = ____
9. 4 x 9 = ____
10. 9 x 10 = ____
12. 2 x 9 = ____
13. 9 x 11 = ____

Down

2. 9 x 3 = ____
3. 6 x 9 = ____
4. 0 x 9 = ____
6. 9 x 8 = ____
8. 7 x 9 = ____
11. 9 x 9 = ____

Around Town

Multiply.

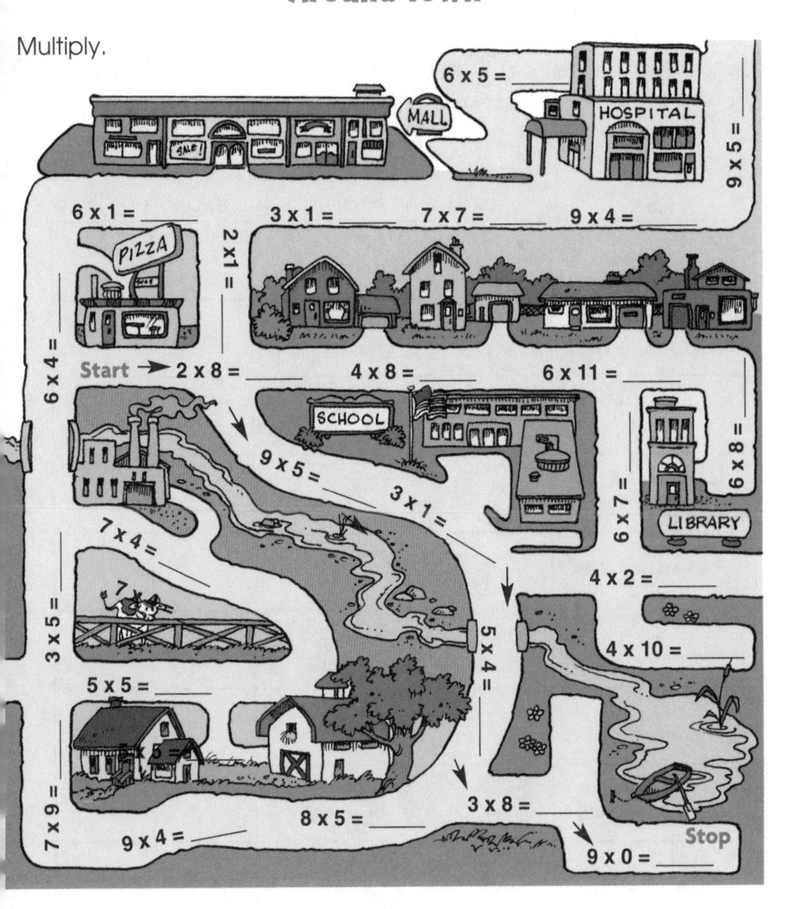

Eager Seeker

Divide the objects and food equally among the groups of people shown below. How many will each person receive? How much will be left over?

ITEM	NUMBER OF PEOPLE	EACH	LEFT OVER
1. 28 MARBLES	3		
2. 15 STICKS OF BUBBLE GUM	4		
3. 8 ONE DOLLAR BILLS	2		
4. 15 SLICES OF PIZZA	3		
5. 4 BALLOONS	2		
6. 25 MARSHMALLOWS	4		
7. 6 TOY DINOSAURS	2		
8. 29 FRENCH FRIES	3		
9. 12 STRAWBERRIES	2		
10. 19 COOKIES	4		

Flag Wagger

Write a fraction for the section of the flag next to the arrow.

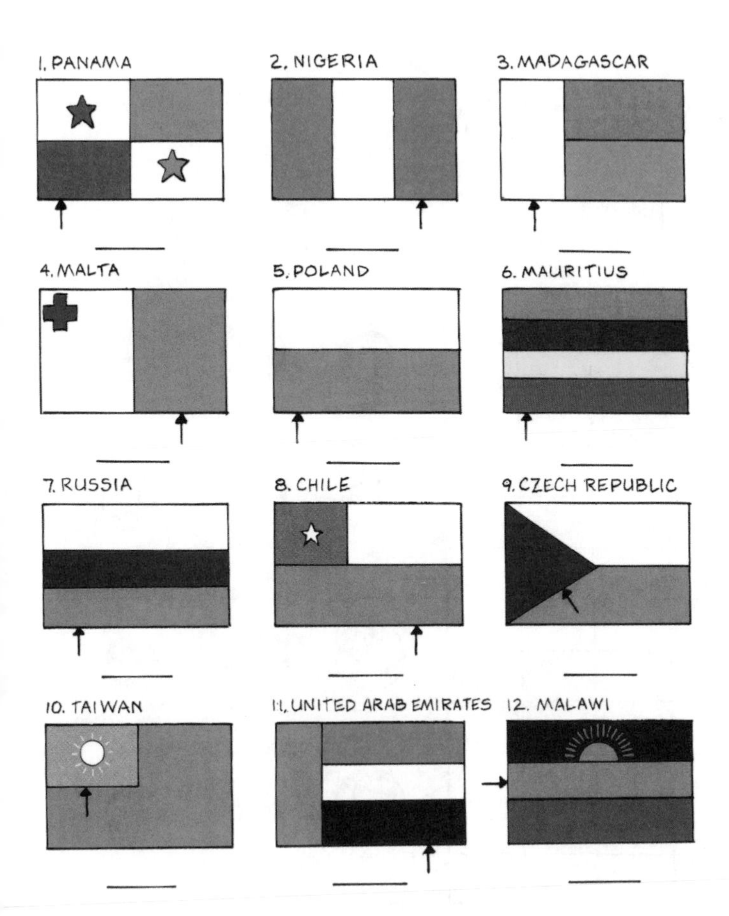

Dollar Scholar

How many ways can you make a dollar? Write the number of coins you will need.

Write how many of each.

	Quarter	Dime	Nickel	Penny
1.				
2.				
3.				
4.				
5.				
6.				
7.				
8.				
9.				
10.				
11.				
12.				
13.				
14.				
15.				

SHOW 63¢ FOUR WAYS.

16. ____ ____ ____

17. ____ ____ ____

18. ____ ____ ____

19. ____ ____ ____